Ian Heath's
DOUBLE-
TALK
FOR BEN AND CHARLOTTE
W.H. ALLEN · LONDON
1985

Printed and bound in Great Britain by
Anchor Brendon Limited, Tiptree, Essex
for the Publishers, W. H. Allen & Co. PLC
44 Hill Street, London W1X 8LB

ISBN 0 491 03771 6

ACCORDING TO RELIABLE SOURCES.....
RUMOUR HAS IT......
NEWS

DARLING THAT WAS ABSOLUTELY FANTASTIC!
YOU'RE ABOUT AS EXCITING AS A PICNIC ON A WET AFTERNOON!

CAN YOU KEEP A SECRET?
I'M TELLING YOU BECAUSE I WANT THE WHOLE WORLD TO KNOW!

I CAN FIND NOTHING WRONG!
YOU'RE A TIME-WASTING HYPOCHONDRIAC!

A SIMPLE, COMFORTABLE HOTEL ONLY A FEW MINUTES FROM THE SEA
...FILTHY ROOMS, LUMPY BEDS AND A TWENTY MINUTES WALK TO THE FOUL-SMELLING BEACH
HOTEL
SUN FUN

THE METER'S JAMMED!
I FORCED A FOREIGN COIN INTO IT!

I'D LIKE TO BE ABLE TO HELP YOU, BUT........
YOU MUST BE JOKING!
BANK

NO!
YES!

IT'LL COST SOMEWHERE ABOUT EIGHTY POUNDS
YOU WON'T SEE MUCH CHANGE FROM THREE HUNDRED QUID!
MOTOR REPAIRS

........MY LEARNED FRIEND....
.....THAT SMUG LITTLE BULLSHITTER....

THIS TASTES ABSOLUTELY DELICIOUS!
CAN'T YOU EVEN FOLLOW THE INSTRUCTIONS ON THE PACKET?

SORRY! THE BRAKES FAILED!
I WAS LOOKING AT THAT GIRL IN THE TIGHT WHITE JEANS!

I'LL REVIEW THE SITUATION IN A FEW WEEKS TIME, TRIMBLE
THE ANSWER IS 'NO' AND IT WILL ALWAYS BE 'NO'!

HE'S WORKING ON A BIG PROJECT IN THE MIDDLE EAST
HE'S DOING FOUR YEARS FOR ARMED ROBBERY!

PLEASE LET ME PAY MY SHARE
IF YOU ALLOW ME TO PAY, I'LL NEVER SEE YOU AGAIN!

I ONLY WORE THEM ONCE AND THE HEEL CAME OFF!
I'VE WORN THEM EVERY DAY FOR THREE WEEKS AND I DON'T LIKE THEM ANYMORE
SHOES
SHOES
SHOES

YOU ARE SO BEAUTIFUL!
PITY ABOUT THE SPOTS ON YOUR BUM!

...ONE CAREFUL WOMAN OWNER, AND ONLY 17,000 MILES!
IT WAS A WRITE-OFF WHICH I BODGED UP, AND I'VE PUT THE CLOCK BACK!
JOES MOTOR
USED CARS

WE HAVE TO GO NOW TO RELIEVE THE BABYSITTER!
WE CANNOT STAND YOUR AWFUL FRIENDS FOR A MINUTE LONGER!

I'VE HEARD SUCH A LOT ABOUT YOU!
I HEAR YOU'RE A NASTY PIECE OF WORK!

MY WIFE DOESN'T UNDERSTAND ME!
MY WIFE CAN READ ME LIKE A FLIPPIN' BOOK!

I'M REALLY ENJOYING OUR DISCUSSION
YOU'RE NOT TOO BRIGHT, BUT WHAT A BOTTOM!

NOT BAD, BUT YOUR THREE-POINT-TURNS NEED PRACTISING!
NEVER IN A HUNDRED YEARS WILL YOU PASS THE TEST!
SCHOOL OF MOTORING

I **ALWAYS** VOTE FOR YOUR PARTY
I DON'T VOTE AND I'M NOT LISTENING TO ALL YOUR BULLSHIT!

I'LL SEE WHAT I CAN DO!
I INTEND DOING NOTHING!

... AND I MEAN THAT SINCERELY
I DON'T ENJOY FIBBING LIKE THIS!

I KEEP THINKING I'M A SNOWDROP!
I'M ONLY HERE BECAUSE YOU'RE SO GOOD-LOOKING!
OF
PSYCHIATRY

I'M SORRY!
I MEANT EVERYTHING I SAID —AND MORE!

SORRY, SIR, BUT WE'RE FULLY BOOKED!
I REMEMBER YOU — YOU DIDN'T LEAVE A TIP LAST TIME!

IT'S NOT RARE AND HAS A SLIGHT CHIP, SO I CAN ONLY OFFER YOU £15 FOR IT!
I CAN GET TWO HUNDRED QUID FOR THIS WITH NO PROBLEM!
ANTIQUES BOUGHT & SOLD
OPEN

GEE, YOUR ACCENT IS SO QUAINT!
I HAVE'N'T UNDERSTOOD A GODDAM WORD SO FAR!
TOURS

IT'S BEEN SO NICE MEETING YOU!
YOU'RE ONE OF THE MOST BORING PEOPLE I'VE EVER COME ACROSS!

I LOVE YOU!
I LOVE SPENDING YOUR MONEY!
FASHION
PARIS
ROME
LONDON
NEW YORK
RIO DE JAN

LOVELY! SUPER! IT'S JUST YOU, DARLING!
I'VE MADE A RIGHT PIGS-EAR OF THIS!

IT'S REALLY VERY SIMPLE
YOU'LL **NEVER** MASTER THIS, YOU INCOMPETENT TWIT!

BOO-HOO! BOO-HOO-HOO!
YIPPEE! I'VE WAITED FORTY-TWO YEARS FOR THIS!
R.I.P.

THE COLOUR'S PERFECT! — IT REALLY LOOKS ELEGANT!
IT DOESN'T EVEN FIT, BUT IT'S A FEW QUID IN COMMISSION!

I ADVISE YOU TO SELL THE HOUSE AND FILE FOR DIVORCE IMMEDIATELY
IF YOU SORT THINGS OUT AMICABLY WITH YOUR HUSBAND I WON'T MAKE A PENNY OUT OF IT!
AND
SOLICITORS

YOU HAVE THE MOST BEAUTIFUL EYES!
YOUR TITS ARE MAGNIFICENT!

I CAN'T SAY FAIRER THAN THAT!
I COULDN'T BE MUCH MORE DISHONEST!

I'LL FIX IT AT THE WEEKEND!
I MAY GET IT DONE BY NEXT CHRISTMAS!

...TOM'S ILL — WE CAN'T COME OVER TONIGHT!
WE'VE BEEN INVITED TO A BETTER PARTY!

I JUST LOVE YOUR TABLE-LAMP!
WHAT DISGUSTING FURNITURE!

I'VE CREATED AN EXCITING NEW POSITION FOR YOU, PERKINS
YOU'RE STUPID, AND I DISLIKE YOU, SO I'M SENDING YOU TO GREENLAND FOR FIVE YEARS!
N SWIMWEAR CO

SHE'S GONE TO THE COUNTRY FOR THE WEEK-END
SHE'S SITTING RIGHT HERE WITH YOUR BEST FRIEND!

EXCUSE ME!
GET OUT OF THE BLASTED WAY!

SO BOLD! SO DYNAMIC! -YET SO VERY SENSITIVE!
WHAT UTTER RUBBISH! MY DOG COULD DO BETTER THAN THAT!

I'VE BEEN A VERY GOOD GIRL, MUMMY!
I WANT SOME SWEETS!

I FEEL FINE, THANKS
APART FROM MY RHEUMATISM, HIGH BLOOD PRESSURE, HEART TROUBLE AND DEPRESSION, I'M ENJOYING GOOD HEALTH!

MARY! FANCY SEEING YOU HERE!
HOW IN THE HELL CAN YOU AFFORD TO SHOP IN THIS PLACE?

MARY'S SO LUCKY TO HAVE FOUND SUCH A GREAT GUY
HOW ON EARTH DID MY DAUGHTER GET INVOLVED WITH SUCH A CREEP?
GOOD LUCK
GOOD LUCK
GOOD LUCK

HE'S ONLY BEING FRIENDLY
GIVEN HALF A CHANCE, HE'LL EAT THAT LITTLE RAT!

BIT NIPPY THIS MORNING?
F****** FREEZING ISN'T IT?!

HELLO! HOW ARE YOU?
PLEASE SPARE ME YOUR LIST OF AILMENTS JUST THIS ONCE!

FIFTY? — I'D HAVE PUT YOU IN YOUR EARLY FORTIES
THANK HEAVENS YOU TOLD ME — I WOULD HAVE GUESSED NEARER SIXTY!

IT'S TOO FRUITY FOR A '73 — GET ME ANOTHER BOTTLE!
THIS WILL IMPRESS HER!

THE CHEQUE'S IN THE POST!
I HAVEN'T SIGNED A CHEQUE FOR SIX MONTHS AND I DON'T INTEND TO START NOW!

WELL PLAYED!
CHEAT!

HE'S SO CUTE! — SO ADORABLE!
MY GOD! WHAT AN UGLY BRUTE!

.......AND I MISSED A HOLE-IN-ONE BY ONLY TWO INCHES
ANOTHER THIRTY FEET AND I'D HAVE REACHED THE GREEN!

DARLING! YOU WERE JUST ABSOLUTELY MARVELLOUS!
HOW ON EARTH DID YOU GET THE PART YOU UNTALENTED BITCH?!

DARLING! IT'S JUST WHAT I'VE ALWAYS WANTED!
I DIDN'T REALISE YOUR TASTE WAS QUITE SO AWFUL!
HAPPY BIRTHDAY

THIS IS A VERY OLD RECIPE GIVEN TO ME BY MY GRANDMOTHER!
IT'S BOEUF STROGANOFF GONE HORRIBLY WRONG!

HONEYBUNCH, THIS IS FOR THIRTY TWO WONDERFUL YEARS TOGETHER!
THIS IS FOR TWO HAPPY YEARS, TWENTY MEDIOCRE ONES AND TEN DIABOLICAL ONES!

I DO LIKE BEING WITH YOU
I LOVE YOUR CRIMSON PORSCHE!

WHAT TIME WILL FATHER CHRISTMAS COME DOWN THE CHIMNEY?
WHEN ARE YOU GOING TO CREEP INTO MY ROOM WITH THE PRESENTS?

IT CAN BE ASSEMBLED IN ABOUT FIFTEEN MINUTES
IF YOU CAN PUT IT TOGETHER WITHIN A WEEK OR TWO, YOU'RE A GENIUS!
EASI-KIT
WARDROBE

YOU'VE BEEN SLEEPING WITH HIM ?!
YOU KIDS HAVE ALL THE FUN !

I SWEAR BY ALMIGHTY GOD TO TELL THE TRUTH, THE WHOLE TRUTH, AND NOTHING BUT THE TRUTH
YOU LOT ARE ABOUT TO HEAR EVERYTHING **BUT** THE TRUTH!

WE MUST KEEP IN TOUCH WHEN WE GET HOME!
MY GOD! — YOU DON'T LIVE THAT CLOSE DO YOU!?!
HOTEL

I'VE ALREADY GIVEN!
I WOULD'N'T DONATE A PENNY TO SUCH AN UNDESERVING CAUSE!

SHE'S SUCH FUN!
ATTENTION-SEEKING LITTLE BITCH!

YOU HAVEN'T CHANGED A BIT!
GOOD GRIEF! YOU'VE GOT SO BLOODY FAT!
BOUTI

YOU'RE LOOKING SO WELL!
SHALL I CALL AN AMBULANCE?

QUALITY VEAL MARINATED IN WINE, GENTLY COOKED IN A GARLIC SAUCE AND SERVED WITH FRESH VEGETABLES
YESTERDAYS LEFTOVERS SMOTH-ERED WITH GARLIC & WINE DREGS, WITH FROZEN PEAS
ENU
MENU

YOU'RE SO ROMANTIC
SOD THE MOON! – LET'S GET ON WITH IT!

...MY PARTY'S TOTALLY COMMITTED TO THE WELFARE OF PENSIONERS
IF I'M ELECTED I WON'T GIVE A MONKEYS ABOUT THE LIKES OF YOU!
VOTE WILK

GO BACK TO THE 'TOAD & TURKEY', TURN LEFT, FOLLOW THE RIVER 'TIL YOU SEE A BARN, FORK RIGHT......
NEVER EVEN HEARD OF THE PLACE!

WISH YOU WERE HERE.....
I SHALL GO AWAY ON MY OWN AGAIN NEXT YEAR!

I HATE YOU!!
I LOVE YOU!

THIS MODEL IS EXTREMELY GOOD VALUE!
WE MAKE MOST PROFIT ON THIS ONE!
ASHING ACHINES
10% OFF
FF!
H.P. TERM
10% OFF!

YOU'RE **NOT** GOING OUT DRESSED LIKE THAT!
I WISH I HAD THE YOUTH AND CONFIDENCE TO WEAR THAT!

HE'S AS WELL AS CAN BE EXPECTED
I DON'T THINK HE'LL MAKE IT THROUGH THE NIGHT!

CLARISSA! WHAT A SUPER STUNNING LITTLE OUTFIT!
WHAT A MESS! HAVE YOU BEEN GOING TO JUMBLE SALES AGAIN?

WHAT YOU SAY MAKES SUCH A LOT OF SENSE
I'VE NEVER HEARD SUCH A LOAD OF OLD CRAP!

OF COURSE I LOVE BEING IN BED WITH YOU
I WONDER WHAT I'M MISSING ON TELLY?

SILENCE

...AND THERE'S A FIFTEEN YEAR MONEY-BACK GUARANTEE!
JUST TRY TRACING US WHEN YOU START HAVING PROBLEMS!
DOUBLE GLAZING

YOU SAY THE NICEST THINGS!
IT'S NOT WORTH A FREE MEAL LISTENING TO YOUR INSINCERE DRIVEL!

I LOVE YOU!
I WANT TO SPEND THE NIGHT WITH YOU!
HOTEL

TAKE TWO OF THESE THREE TIMES A DAY
I HAVEN'T A CLUE WHAT'S THE MATTER WITH YOU!

.....SOME SUNNY PERIODS WITH OCCASIONAL SHOWERS.....
JUST WAIT AND SEE — I DON'T KNOW!

OF COURSE I REMEMBER YOU!
NEVER SEEN YOU BEFORE IN MY LIFE!

THIS IS YOUR CAPTAIN SPEAKING – WE HAVE A MINOR FAULT IN ONE OF THE ENGINES
GOODBYE EVERYBODY!